CW01083640

Stress Related Disorders

ILLNESS: AN INTELLIGENT ACT OF THE BODY

By

Allen Lawrence, M.A., M.D., Ph.D.

And

Lisa Robyn Lawrence, M.S., Ph.D.

Allco Publishing
Tarzana, California

ACKNOWLEDGMENTS

Many thanks to Mary Embree our editor for her editing skills and support. Her efforts are highly appreciated and her contribution was extremely valuable.

The cover picture was created for us by Jane McKinney of Ojai, California. Thank you Jane, it is beautiful.

This book is dedicated to the thousands of patients we have worked with over the years for truly none of this work could have been done without you. You have been our teachers and our guides. It is only through working with you that we have had the opportunity to learn and grow and be sufficiently challenged to reach higher than we thought was possible. This book and all that we publish are for you, without you we would have no reason to write.

This book is also dedicated to Mom Sally for her help and moral support.

(Pages which are left blank are done so on purpose.)

TABLE OF CONTENTS

FORWARD

Each year tens of thousands of men, women and children suffer and even die from illnesses that are caused by stress. Until recently the medical profession has practically ignored these illnesses and, unfortunately, the people who suffer from them.

The following text is part of a series of works which will help define the many faces of the illnesses which are presently either not recognized or not fully understood by the medical profession. This work is dedicated to defining the origins of Stress-Related Disorders (SRDs), that is, illnesses that are caused by or made worse by stress. In other presentations we will look at other areas which cause illnesses that frequently go unrecognized by the medical profession. We will cover topics such as stress, relationships, nutrition, the crucial life transitions as well as transpersonal causes, spiritual crisis and the relationship of our decisions and the forces of the birth process which ultimately create illness.

We hope that you will not only enjoy this book and the others to come, but that you will be able to use them to help solve the mysteries and problems of your life. Hopefully, they will help you heal old wounds, overturn present illnesses and help you regain wellness. We trust that they will help in your own personal growth by adding to your understanding of our Intelligent Universe.

INTRODUCTION

For the past twenty-five years I (Allen) have been a medical doctor. Most of those years were spent practicing Standard or Interventive Medicine (the "when you get broken, we fix you" form of medicine). While the services that Standard-Interventive Medicine provides are important and extremely valuable to our society, this format did not allow me to really help people the way I wanted. When I first started practicing medicine, I thought that medicine was about curing people and returning them to optimal wellness. The assumption was that this did not mean keeping them on medication for the balance of their lives.

Fourteen years ago Lisa and I began to teach people how to eat better, solve health problems and resolve illness, as part of my medical practice. The results were exciting and stimulated us to learn more about how to heal people rather than to just treat their symptoms. Unfortunately we soon found that the 15 minutes or less, per patient, format of standard medical practice was incompatible with being able to give people the information they needed to help them reverse their illnesses. This experience brought about the realization that it was time to leave the practice of Interventive Medicine and work primarily with Healing people.

We now work primarily with people who suffer from illnesses which are not treatable in the Standard-Interventive medical system. This was necessary for our personal growth as well as to heal ourselves and reach for *our highest and best Selves*.

In our present mode of practice we dedicate our time to four goals. Our primary goal is to heal people. We do this by helping people find and resolve the conflicts and problems of their life that have caused their illnesses. Generally, we work with people who want to get well but who have neither been healed nor obtained the results they desired from the present medical system. Experience has taught us that many of these people may already be aware that they are suffering from stress but do not understand its role in creating their present illnesses. Our intention is not just to treat illness but to cure it. We seek to reverse its affects and assist the formerly sick person to learn what the illness was about and help them grow into a stronger more complete person from the process.

Our second goal is to prevent illness. We do this by working in the community, through our practice to educate and consult in the areas of stress and Stress-Related Disorders, on the-job stress and other stresses. Our third goal is to teach people how to heal their own illnesses, eliminate stress and reach for their highest and best Self. Our fourth goal is to write about stress, wellness, healing, Huna (the ancient Hawaiian healing system) and relationships. These four goals are a part of a process we believe is necessary to heal our community and the individuals within it.

STRESS-RELATED DISORDERS

We call what we do Integrated Medicine (that is "you heal yourself long before you get sick" medicine). Integrated medicine differs from Interventive medicine by looking for the causes of illness as not being outside of us but rather coming from within. It helps us understand the power of our thoughts and beliefs. With this knowledge we can see how our negative thoughts interact within our immune, healing and repair systems by disturbing them and ultimately causing them to malfunction. Integrated medicine contains findings from the field of *Psychoneuroimmunobiology*, medicine's newest interdisciplinary field. This new discipline is designed to integrate biology, physics and many other scientific disciplines with medical science. The primary goal of this new field is to solve the health problems that medicine, working on its own, has not been able to solve. Integrated medicine differs from Interventive medicine in that it is not based on treatment with drugs or surgery but depends on problem solving and education to prevent illness from occurring in the first place.

Integrated Medicine involves the integration of mind, body and spirit to heal illness. It mobilizes the innate healing powers of the mind-body. Integrated Medicine is based on helping people find and integrate their healing powers before they get sick and hence prevent them from getting sick. It also teaches people how to learn and grow from their illnesses if they have become sick.

To accomplish our goals we must *work only with people who are ready to make a difference in their own life*. The people we work with must have a substantial willingness to create wellness and do what is necessary to change their life and get well. We believe that there are people everywhere who not only want to get well, but who are also ready to grow emotionally and spiritually.

At the foundation of our understanding of healing is the belief that the *Universe is Intelligent,* our *Mind is Intelligent* and *our Body is Intelligent*. The healing process begins only when the individual chooses to become healed. The role of the healer is to act as a facilitator to help the ill person integrate the three Intelligence (the conscious self, the unconscious self and the supraconscious or spiritual self) which already exist within each of us. Health and wellness is our natural state. All that is necessary for individuals to reclaim health and wellness is to know how to draw it out of themselves. Lisa and I will help anyone who is ready and willing to make this journey.

People often ask what we do that is different from the Interventive physician. The Interventive physician treats the body and the body alone, primarily through the use of drugs and surgery. We direct our attention to the whole person and help them resolve their problems whether they are physical, mental or spiritual. We work with the individual's own innate healing and balancing mechanisms. We balance and integrate rather than treat with drugs or surgery. We help individuals activate their healing systems. While healing through the three Selves does not require medications, drugs, herbs or other external treatments, they can be used along with a patient's present treatment program to support it and make it more effective. Finding truth in one's life, eating a healthy diet, proper relaxation and exercise and, most importantly, elimination of stresses are the essential aspects of our work.

Through Integrated Medicine, we help people help themselves to get well and stay well.

Allen Lawrence, M.D., Ph.D.
Lisa Robyn Lawrence, M.S., Ph.D.

CHAPTER I

WELLNESS LOST: STRESS AS AN INTELLIGENT ACT OF THE BODY

WHAT IS WELLNESS?

Wellness is defined in the dictionary as "a state of well being, health and prosperity." How many of us truly feel well, healthy and prosperous? In our present society the fact that we are healthy today does not preclude becoming ill tomorrow. Many people have health problems, physical or emotional symptoms that deprive them of wellness. The two big questions of our time are how can we maintain our present health, wellness and prosperity and how can we return to wellness if we are already sick?

To answer both of these questions we must first understand why so many of us get sick. We must learn what the medical profession doesn't know and may not want to know. We will need to understand the relationship between stress and illness and how we create stress in our lives. Since stress robs us of our well-being and health, we must learn to recognize our own personal stresses and find ways to eliminate them. In the end, we cannot protect ourselves from illness, maintain our wellness or reestablish wellness and good health without understanding how stress causes illness.

**ILLNESS
IS UNNECESSARY**

To understand how people get sick we must first understand that wellness is our normal state, our birthright. Illness is not normal, rather it is a state which occurs only when *we* have not protected ourselves optimally. This is not to place blame on anyone who is sick; we recognize that what we are about to tell you is not taught to us by parents, teachers, medical doctors, nor society in general. As we proceed it is likely that you will recognize that everything we need to help protect ourselves from illness is already known to us and that this information is entirely about common sense solutions to the problems which cause stress and diminish our wellness.

**WELLNESS IS
THE NATURAL STATE OF MAN**

STRESS AS A CAUSE OF ILLNESS

Recent studies have suggested that between 70% and 80% of all health problems seen in the medical doctor's office are either caused by or related to stress. However, neither the general public nor the medical profession is really aware of what stress is or how it actually affects us. In the following pages we will show you how the Survival Mandate, which operates through the Stress Mechanism and is built into all living creatures, is at the root of almost all illnesses we suffer from. See Table 1, below.

Any medical or health problem which is related to or caused by stress can be referred to as a *Stress-Related Disorder*™. While most commonly stress precedes illness, it makes no difference which has come first. Once illness occurs, for whatever reason, stress is also generated.

Table: 1. Illnesses or Conditions Related to Stress	
<ul><li>Headaches</li><li>Mood swings</li><li>Muscle tension</li><li>Anxiety</li><li>Depression</li><li>Insomnia</li><li>Nervousness</li><li>Fatigue</li><li>Apathy</li><li>Hypertension (high blood pressure)</li></ul>	<ul><li>Infections</li><li>Chest pains</li><li>Many types of heart disease</li><li>Stomach pains</li><li>Indigestion</li><li>Ulcers</li><li>Colitis</li><li>Chronic constipation</li><li>Muscle, joint and body pains</li><li>Recurrent colds and flus</li></ul>
These are just a few of the conditions or illnesses which can be considered Stress-Related Disorders™, either caused by or related to stress.	

Women may also find themselves suffering additional symptoms such as menstrual pain, premenstrual syndrome, menstrual irregularities, post-partum depression and other gynecologic problems that are either caused by or worsened by stress. Many gynecologic problems not previously related to stress can now be recognized to be caused by the stress of unresolved conflicts relating to femininity, sexuality and issues of male vs. female power. The same is true of men, including problems involving the prostate, testicles and other aspects of the generative organs. These problems and many other common health problems and their symptoms rob millions of men and women of their vitality and feelings of wellness each year[1].

Unfortunately, large numbers of people live their entire lives suffering from problems they should not have to endure. Many people are not aware that the secret of good health and well-being lies within the way they live their lives and what they believe about themselves, their bodies and their illnesses. Our stresses directly or indirectly affect our immune, healing and repair systems as well as our lifestyle, how and what we eat and how much exercise we get. They also affect our will to live or die, what we think about ourselves, the decisions we make and the belief systems we hold. Knowing how to manage our life and reduce our stresses can make a great difference in our lives.

During the course of this text we will look at two models. The first will be the Wellness-Stress-Illness Model. This model will show us how stress, if not resolved, can lead to illness. The second model we will look at is the Stress-Illness- Wellness model. It will teach us how we can reverse the illness process and return to wellness. Together these models will help us recognize the warning signals that can alert us to the stress we experience as well as how illness is created and reversed. We will use these models to explain how our mind, body and spirit act independently and together to cause and cure illness.

Finally, we will demonstrate how our belief systems and the decisions we make are ultimately responsible for most of our stresses and problems. Through understanding these processes and how they work, we can learn to change the way we think and to construct more positive belief systems. And this can only help to improve the quality of our lives and our overall health and well-being.

CHOOSING WELLNESS

Our overall level of wellness, to a great degree, is dependent upon our state of mind and the belief systems we hold. As

Abraham Lincoln once said, "Most people are just about as happy as they make up their mind to be."

What we believe about yourself, our life and the world around us acts as a kind of filter, a filter, which controls the way, we see the world. Because of this each of us live entirely within our own separate reality. How we construct this reality affects the decisions we subsequently make.

For example, when we choose not to eat right, when we don't like ourselves or when we are negative about ourselves, we are holding and empowering negative thoughts about ourselves. We call these negative self-thoughts *Death Wishes* since they are the basis of beliefs which can or encourage the "death" or distortion of our wellness and well-being. On the other hand, the beliefs and decisions which ultimately promote our wellness, health, emotional and physical well-being we think of as *Life Wishes*.

Life wishes are easily recognized for they enhance the quality of our life, make us feel better about yourself and promote habits which lead to greater physical, mental, emotional and spiritual well-being. The goal of all therapy and healing work is to identify the *death wishes* we hold and the specific beliefs that potentiate them. They then must be converted into *life wishes* by making new decisions and new life choices. If one does not experience complete wellness and well-being then it is likely that a *death wish is* at the root of his condition.

STRESS AND THE FIGHT OR FLIGHT MECHANISM

Stress is a state of physical and emotional tension (pressure) that occurs in response to the events or situations in our lives. It is the result of a larger bodily process which is designed to protect us from any kind of harm: The Fight or Flight Response. Basically, the stress process is triggered whenever we are threatened. This can occur whether the events or situations are real and presently occurring or whether they are potential threats. Stress can also occur when a threat is imagined and not real. While the process is designed to ensure our survival, it can often work against us. In our present society the stress response is often triggered by events and situations which have little or nothing to do with our immediate or long-term survival.

Primitive humans could not have survived in the jungle without this kind of instinctive mandate. For example, consider a prehistoric man walking in the jungle and hearing a noise behind him. He could have chosen to ignore it, but if it had been a tiger it could have attacked him and killed him. (We certainly wouldn't want that to happen for he could have been our great-great-great-grandparent.) He could also have responded to the threat by either turning and fighting the tiger or by running away from it. This is the basis of the stress mechanism: Fight or Flight. If he runs away or fights he may survive, but if he has to stop to think about what to do, it is likely he would have been eaten. Once threatened, he learns from that experience. Any time in the future he hears a noise in the jungle (or possibly anywhere else) he is most likely going to think it's a tiger until proven otherwise.

The Stress Mechanism is an innate and automatic response system that protects us from the many potentially hostile forces which surround us. It is generally triggered long before we are consciously aware that we are being threatened. The condition we think of as stress is made up of a combination of physical, emotional, bio-chemical, hormonal and neurologic reactions within our body. For the most part, stress is a way in which we react to the events and conditions of our external environment and not the events themselves. Our stresses are generally triggered by what we think and feel internally rather than events outside of us. It can also triggered by instincts, those pre-planned survival programs which lie deep within our unconscious self, often at the level of the genetic codes of our DNA.

Many of us are often *under stress*. Yet the number of genuine life threatening situations we experience in our life are generally few. Most of the time when we experience stress we are reacting to the events, situations and beliefs of our life, just as if they are *tigers*.

When we talk about *stress*, most of the time we are really talking about *Negative Stress*. Negative stress causes negative feelings and internal sensations. However, stress is not always negative. There is also *Positive Stress*, that is, *stress* which produces positive feelings and internal sensations as their end result. Negative stresses might be situations like being involved in an auto accident, losing a job, or the death of a friend or parent. A positive stress might be winning a lottery, being promoted to a higher position or the arrival of a new baby in the home. Any of these negative situations could end up with positive results and any of the positive situations could end up being negative. Therefore, *stress* is more often related to how we interpret the events of our life than it is to the actual events themselves.

Imagine yourself sitting under a palm tree on a tropical isle looking up at lazy white clouds drifting slowly across a bright blue sky. Nowhere to go. Nothing to do. You have the whole day to just relax, rest and enjoy life. Some of you might be thinking, "How am I going to get the money to travel to a tropical island?" "How could I go with all that I have to do here?" "Doing nothing sounds so boring." Others would just get into the picture and enjoy the feelings of being in such a situation. Most of the day-to-day stress we experience is created by what we think and believe and how we use our thoughts to react to the world around us.

NEGATIVE STRESS CAUSES FAILURE

While positive stress can stimulate us to be a better student, a better athlete or help us through college and other such positive things, negative stress is always destructive. Positive stress is often the driving force in creating healthy relationships and advancing to the highest levels of our life. Negative stress disrupts and destroys relationships and the substance of our life. While positive stress has been referred to as *competition, drive* or even *push* by those who use it to better themselves, negative stress is always related to failure. This propensity to fail is because negative stress leads to more negative stress and is often the triggering mechanism for negative processes.

STRESS AS A MATTER OF FAULTY BELIEFS

Although few of us will actually experience life threatening situations in our day-to-day life, constant stress is quite common. The stress mechanism is there to protect us from threats to our life and limb, however, it can in fact be triggered by anything that is even remotely interpreted by our inner self as a threat. This includes our own beliefs and belief systems. It is not unusual for people to have belief systems that act as a threat to themselves. Fear of failure. Fear of a parent or boss. Fear of not getting what we want in life or fear of losing what we already have. Feeling unhappy with ourselves, low self-esteem or anger. Any belief or thought which we hold that potentially acts as a threat to who and what we really are can trigger the stress mechanism. In fact, most of the stress that people experience is caused by their own faulty belief systems.

To best appreciate what stress is we have developed a simple definition to describe it: Stress is a complex of physical, emotional, spiritual, chemical and hormonal signs and symptoms created by *the difference between the way we want our world to be and the way the world actually is.* Using this definition you will soon see how stress can lead to illness. Stress most commonly occurs as an automatic response. It is also often created by us in the way we choose to see the world we live in and how we react to it.

> ### STRESS IS THE DIFFERENCE
> ### BETWEEN THE WAY WE WANT
> ### THE WORLD TO BE AND THE
> ### WAY IT IS

For example: Joe only has $50 in his checking account but he very much wants some new clothes totaling $250. In order to buy the clothes right now, Joe writes a check, hoping that the money will somehow arrive before his check reaches the bank. He doesn't have to write the check. He could wait until he has the money in the bank. He could have even managed his affairs better so the money would have been in the bank. By writing the check with insufficient funds, Joe has created the stress he is about to experience. In this case it was intentional, because he knew better and he had other choices. Contrast this with the following example. You're standing in line at your bank and an armed robber comes in and holds it up. You suddenly feel stress. This is a stress that you didn't intentionally create. This response is natural and instinctive under these circumstances.

WHAT ARE THE OVERALL EFFECTS OF STRESS?

Whether stress is self-provoked and intentional or entirely unintentional on our part makes no difference to our body. Our body reacts in exactly the same manner to both situations. With the recognition of a threat, no matter the cause, the Fight or Flight Response mechanism is activated. Biochemical and nervous system pathways are stimulated and the neuro-hormones of stress are released to ready the body for either flight or fight. The process is designed to protect us against threats to our life or well-being, no matter what causes them.

Once stress is triggered, it immediately creates a number of changes in our body. It stimulates our heart, increases our heartbeat and raises our blood pressure. Blood is shifted away from the digestive tract and is sent to the muscle systems of our body. Our hands become cold and clammy, our throat becomes dry, breathing becomes more rapid and a general sense of anxiety and muscular tension begins to build up within us. We may experience an urgency to act, to make a decision or do some-thing. In such situations people often make decisions they later regret. This is how Stress-Related Disorders™ are born.

If the stressful situation is over quickly the physical and chemical changes will rapidly reverse and soon dissipate. If, however, the stress persists or there are multiple stressors (of one or more events or situations which we perceive as threatening) over a prolonged period of time, the body becomes overly stimulated and chronic tension remains. When this happens, we learn to expect stress in our life. We recognize this as a generalized state of anxiety and it is the basis of the Dis-Stress process which we will talk about in the next chapter.

When the negative or faulty belief systems and unresolved problems occur they often challenge our *ideal self-image* or *ideal self-picture.* Our ideal-self-image is the picture we hold deep within us of who we are and how we fit into the world around us. This breach creates a state of conflict which acts as a threat to who we believe we are and how we fit in the world around us.

This threat, real or imagined, triggers our stress response system. If, within a short period of time, we can resolve these differences and the problems and conflicts they create, the threat will be removed and the stress reaction will be reversed.

If, however, they are left unresolved then we are left with a residual of internal physical, emotional and psychological tension. The result is negative stress. When we have one or more unresolved conflicts this can soon lead to a state of chronic tension and stress. Since our conflicts are usually based on our personal belief systems, they are just thoughts, and we can decide to select or reject them. We can choose what we want to believe. All we need to do to dispose of these negative or faulty beliefs is to replace them with positive, constructive beliefs. Negative stress is then transformed into positive drive. This is the basis of our stress elimination process. In fact, this should be the basis of all stress education and elimination programs. Unfortunately, it is not.

General information about stress along with techniques of how to eliminate it are easily learned. However, how to transform our stresses from problems into *opportunities* or *challenges* is rarely taught and yet this is the most important element for eliminating stress. When we can transform our stresses into challenges we ultimately make ourselves stronger and hence, greatly improve our quality of life.

The specific physical, mental, emotional and spiritual signs and symptoms of stress are all *clues* that allow us learn more about ourselves and our negative thoughts and beliefs. Many people have spent years trying to find out what their negative forces were and what caused them to have physical, emotional, mental or spiritual problems. Now much of this can be sped up and even bypassed by learning a series of techniques on how to recognize and transform these forces which once caused pain and suffering into positive challenges and opportunities.

> MOST OF THE STRESS
> WE EXPERIENCE ON A DAY-TO-DAY BASIS
> IS CAUSED BY OUR OWN FAULTY
> BELIEF SYSTEMS.

HOW DOES STRESS LEAD TO ILLNESS AND DISEASE?

In the previous section we stated that stress is a reaction to the situations and events of our life. Stress, in itself, is not bad but when misinterpreted or allowed to persist without resolution it can form a kind of abnormal stress. A small amount of stress, or stress in "normal" amounts, stimulates the body's immune-defensive and healing system. If we are injured, the triggering of the stress system stimulates our internal defensive systems and turns on our healing mechanisms. However, once the degree of the stress we experience exceeds normal amounts, it may result in breakdown and deterioration. The exact amount of stress that will cause this to happen varies greatly from individual to individual and situation to situation. It is often related to the total amount of stress, our overall attitude and whether we are operating from life wishes or death wishes.

THE THREE SELVES

Most modern day Western Standard Interventive medical practitioners think of their patients as biologic machines, which once broken require fixing. Hence for the past 350 years the body, its chemistry and anatomy have been the major focus of the medical practitioner. Much less important has been the patient's mind as to its relationship to getting sick or returning to wellness. The spiritual aspect of the individual is rarely considered meaningful. To many, anything relating to spirits, is simply irrelevant and is left to the clergy to maintain dominion over.

Those of us who practice Integrated medicine see that our mind, body and spirit have significant roles in both the creation and healing of illness. In order to fully understand the relationship and interaction of mind, body and spirit we must go outside of Western medical thought. We must look for a system that parallels Western thinking, a system that is not complicated nor too foreign to our way of thinking. Max Freedom Long, an American teacher and scholar, who rediscovered Huna, provides us with just a system. Huna is an ancient Polynesian and Hawaiian system of healing. Practiced in isolation for four to ten thousand years in the Pacific, Huna not only lends itself easily to our Western thinking but in fact answers questions that previously seemed unanswerable. Huna also provides us with several new ways to look at old problems of Standard Interventive medicine.

The first and possibly most important idea is that of the three Selves. To the Huna master each person is made up of three Selves or three levels of consciousness. These three Selves have been known to us as mind, body and spirit. However, there has been little understanding in our society of mind and spirit. Many of the attributes of these aspects are alluded to in most of the great works of mankind including the Old and New Testaments, the Upanishads and the mysteries of the ancient world. It was not until the clear, concise descriptions of the ancient Hawaiian healing system were unearthed that we were able to really understand their role in the creation and healing of illness.

The first of the three selves, the oldest and most primitive, is the *Lower Self.* It can also be thought of as the unconscious, inner self or the consciousness of the body. In Huna the lower self is essentially a robot or servant which takes orders from the middle self, the second of the three selves.

The *Middle Self,* or the *spirit that talks* as it is known in Huna, is our personality. It is the *I* or *me* that we think of when we think about ourselves. While the middle self sees, hears and thinks, our sensory system, eyes, ears and brain belongs to the lower self. Only the *interpretations* of the sensory system belong to the middle self.

The third self is the *Higher Self.* The Higher Self is our connection to the Intelligence of the Universe. While the lower and middle selves are part of the body-mind located within the body, the Higher Self, is located outside of the body. To the Hawaiians the complete integration and balance of the three selves is the primary factor in creating and maintaining our personal health and wellness. An imbalance or breakdown within either the lower self (the physical body) or the middle self (the personality- ego) leads to illness[2].

Illness occurs in several ways but the two most important are injury caused by sins and the integration of lies or faulty belief systems into the middle and lower selves. The Huna master believed that there was one and only one sin. It was *the causing of intentional harm or hurt to another or one's own self.* When either a sin or a lie exists, this then blocks the ability of the lower self to communicate with the Higher Self and therefore limits our capacity to heal ourselves.

This occurs because we store all of our information about ourselves and the world around us in the lower self. When we hold faulty beliefs, and we know that they are not the truth, we create what the Huna master called *complexes* or *"eating creatures."* These "eating creatures" block us from knowing the truth of who we really are. They also act as filters through which we see the world. This means that our middle self is seeing a distorted or tainted view of our selves. This gap between the way the world really is and the way the middle self sees it almost automatically creates a threat to the lower self which ultimately knows the truth of who and what we are and how we fit into the world. This difference activates the stress mechanism.

Sin works in a similar way, but is slightly different. When we create a sin it leads to guilt. This guilt becomes a threat to our true nature and it ultimately activates the stress mechanism. While the entire mechanism is considerably more complex, all we need to know at this point is that this the basis of how illness occurs.

Stress occurs in the lower self as part of the survival instinct and is often created because the middle self has such a short attention span and awareness of the truths of our life. It is also created because the middle self doesn't like pain or feeling bad. Therefore, when conflict arises it gets pushed down into the lower self. Implicit is the hope that the lower self will solve the problem. The middle self may neither want nor be able to solve its problems. In this case the problems, along with the pain of the events and hence the immediacy to solve the problem at hand, are repressed or submerged out of the reach of the middle self.

The lower self, wanting the problem to be solved and its inner pain to go away[3], pushes its knowledge of the conflict up into the middle self. The middle self experiences only sudden emotions, physical symptoms and other mental or emotional signs of the conflict. If the middle self knows what is happening it can work on and solve the problem. This would relieve the burden of the lower self and help restore harmony by eliminating the problem. When it does not or cannot do this, either because it is unwilling or is dealing with another, more acute problems, the pressure gradually increases. As soon as this process registers as a threat the stress mechanism is activated.

LIES

In an ideal world we would always work and live in truth. We would tell the truth, hear only the truth and believe only the truth. We would tell and accept only the truth for yourself, or as Shakespeare put it, "to thine own self be true." In the real world, however, we often tell lies, we believe the lies of others and we lie so often to ourselves and others that our lower self is almost never sure of when we will lie. When we lie to ourselves or others we always know that we are doing it. Our middle self may want to believe these lies but our lower self knows better. (This is the basis of lie detector testing.)

Each lie that we tell ourselves, or that we tell to others is a hurt that we create in our self or in others. Think of how hurt people are when they find out that someone is lying to them. Over the years these hurts build and guilt and shame are created. It is not unusual for people to lie so much that they ultimately lose the true sense of who they are.

Often the lies we have told our self begin to filter how we see the world around us. We may eventually see everyone around us as not to be believed. We may stop knowing who or what to trust. We may see evil and danger everywhere. A common result is fear and often even depression. Many people lose the capacity to love themselves. When these things happen, the world ultimately becomes a dangerous place.

Our faulty belief systems, lies, fears and guilt influence how we perceive the circumstance and conditions of our life. The end result is stress and while stress may vary from day to day, hour to hour and month to month it generally continues to increase and grows until it not only affects the body, but ultimately, injures it.

THE WELLNESS-STRESS-ILLNESS MODEL

It is essential to be aware that when stress is left unresolved it can lead to illness and then disease4[4]. However, one rarely jumps directly from wellness to disease. Instead, this transformation is more likely to take place over an extended period of time and often progressing slowly through a series of steps. A clear understanding of these steps and the mechanism through which they work is crucial. It allows us, physician and patient, to take charge of this process as well as learn how to stop it and even reverse it.

The following steps make up the basis of a new model for looking at how illness is created. We refer to the model as the *Wellness-Stress-Illness Mechanism*. It is the mechanism by which wellness is converted into illness via the stress response. The schematic for this model is demonstrated in Figure: 1. In the following pages we will look at the flow of events which convert a well person into a sick person.

Initially the individual is healthy and well. Then situations occur which are associated with either faulty beliefs, lies, guilt, fears or the creation of sins. This now creates problems or conflicts that require resolution. These conflicts can occur at any point in the individual's life from decisions made in the uterus, during infancy, childhood, adolescence, teen years and young adulthood, through old age. If, for whatever reason, these problems and conflicts are left unresolved, stress is created and tension builds.

WELLNESS-STRESS-ILLNESS MECHANISM

WELLNESS –> CONFLICT –> STRESS –>

DIS-STRESS –> DIS-EASE –>

DISEASE –> CHRONIC DISEASE –>

DEATH

Figure: 1.

As tension increases it signals an increasing level of threat. This threat then stimulates the stress mechanism and initiates a progressive spiral of increased tension, threat and stress. This often occurs without our conscious awareness.

If the problems are resolved at any time during the process then the stress mechanism reverses, tension is relieved and the body-mind returns to normal. If not, the process continues and the deepest level of the Stress Mechanism, the Intelligence of the Body, is triggered. The Intelligence of the Body activates a mending process which begins first with trying to accept the stress and allow it exist, this is what is generally referred to as *coping.*

Up to this point the conscious mind may have been hiding the knowledge of the conflict from itself, suppressing and burying all conscious awareness of this process. However, even though the conscious mind does not want to deal with the issues which underlie the growing stress, the Intelligence of the body soon beginnings to be forced to recognize the elevating levels of tension caused by the persistent or increasing stress and do something about it. While this increasing level of tension can be sustained for relatively long periods of time, eventually it becomes unacceptable. The lower self is called upon to initiate a process of communicating to the middle self what is happening. The lower self knows that, if this situation is allowed to persist, injury and damage may result. The body-mind wants the conflict resolved and it will soon begin doing whatever it can to resolve the ongoing conflict.

As the Stress-Illness process moves the individual toward higher and higher levels of abnormal or chronic stress, the first definable pattern of events, which we refer to as the Dis-Stress stage, soon becomes recognizable. At the point where the Dis-Stress phase begins, the Intelligence of the Body has initiated an organized process of attempting to communicate directly to the individual through a series of

Intelligent *signs* and *symptoms*.

At first these signs and symptoms are vague and barely discernable. However, if not listened to they will gradually become louder and louder until they eventually get our attention, make us recognize what is happening and realize that we must solve the problems causing our stress. If we don't pay attention, the body then escalates this process. The body wants the conflict resolved and will do whatever is needed to get our attention. If the conflict persists, the process will eventually move the individual to the next level of abnormality, the stage of Dis-Ease.

Dis-Ease is a higher level of maladaption to chronic stress. If the conflict which has led to stress is identified and resolved then this process can be reversed. If not, then the process will persist until it reaches the level we know as Disease. The same rules appear to apply to the state of Disease. If its originating conflict is discovered and resolved then the process will be reversed and the individual will return to wellness once again. If not, it may continue to progress until it reaches the next higher level, the stage of Chronic Disease. Here for the first time tissues are irreversibly damaged and from this point on the process is no longer entirely reversible. Finally, if the process is not stopped, it can lead to the ultimate conclusion, Death.

These are the basic steps of how illness is created and progresses into disease, then eventually chronic disease. For the most part this process is the same whether we are talking about physical, mental, emotional or spiritual Stress-Related Disorders™. Only the specific symptoms and the way they manifest themselves will differ. All are mediated through the stress mechanism. In each case faulty belief systems, lies, guilt, fear, or assumed sins or shame are at the root of the illness. In the following chapters we will discuss each stage in greater detail outlining the factors involved, how they can be recognized, and what can be done about them.

SUMMARY

Through an intelligent process, which we often think of as illness, our body-mind first warns and then finally shouts at us that we have unresolved conflicts, guilt, shame, fears caused by faulty beliefs, lies or sins. This process is mediated through the stress system. In this case stress is secondary to unresolved conflicts and stress can be eliminated simply by resolving the conflicts which have triggered this Wellness-Stress-Illness process.

CHAPTER II

THE DIS-STRESS STAGE

WHAT IS DIS-STRESS?

Everyone has stress in their life. It is not really possible to live life and not have some stress. Positive stress generally does not concern us for it is most often interpreted as good and takes us toward positive and healthy goals. Negative stress, on the other hand, can be and often is a major problem to our health and vitality. The difference between negative and positive stress is ultimately how we let the events of our life affect us. For example, having a noisy neighbor could lead us to sleepless nights, anger and verbal confrontation. All of this will make our heart race, blood pressure rises and our stomach tighten up into knots. This is negative stress. The same situation when looked at positively could present an opportunity to test our skills of negotiation, make a new friend, or help us decide to move. We can either see our stresses as enemies (tigers) or as challenges to improve ourselves.

If we run from our problems (flight) and ignore or suppress them, then we will allow them to turn inward to create chronic stress, anxiety, tension and eventually illness or disease. If we deal with them and solve our problems (fight) it is likely we will grow from the experience. In the end, stress can be either productive or nonproductive[5]. Stress itself is not our enemy but a natural part of life which can often be a friend and teacher depending on how we deal with it.

**STRESS,
IF NOT RESOLVED,
LEADS TO DISTRESS.**

Stress when handled poorly, misinterpreted, left unresolved, not understood or not used to our best advantage is eventually transformed into physical, mental, emotional or spiritual distress. When our stress reaches this stage, we refer to it as *Dis-Stress*. This is the abnormal form of stress which is what people often think of as *Stress.* Dis-Stress is always negative and, if not resolved, frequently leads to illness or disease.

The illnesses associated with Dis-Stress are most likely caused either by injury or disturbance of the chemistry and homeostasis of the body and its tissues and organs. It can cause alterations in the body's ability to defend itself from invaders or parasites and undermine its own defensive system. The stress mechanism mediates the entire Defense and Repair Systems of the body and therefore is directly or indirectly in control of them.

Stressors or events that trigger stress can either be short-term (minutes to weeks) or long-term (months to years) in nature. When we are unable to cope with either short- or long-term stresses the defensive and healing systems of the body are disturbed. The resulting disturbance in their function is eventually recognized by the body's monitoring systems. At first the body will try to adjust and compensate for the destructive changes. Then it will try to reestablish proper function. If it can do this fast enough, it will be unlikely that we will have had an inkling of what has gone on. However, if the body is unable to reestablish function fast enough it is likely that we will experience some intermittent or vague bodily sensations such as muscle aches, tension, headaches, upset stomach, nausea, diarrhea, dizziness, fatigue or simply, just not feeling well. These symptoms may last only minutes to a few hours and may come and go without apparent reason or cause. If, however, our body cannot return its defensive, healing and/or repair system to normal, the body will initiate a process of trying to communicate to the conscious self that something is wrong.

This is demonstrated by the onset of the signs and symptoms of the Dis-Stress stage. The symptoms and signs associated with the Dis-Ease stage are similar in nature but tend to be more pronounced and may often last for longer periods of time. The body's ability to heal itself continues throughout the Dis-Stress and Dis-Ease stages. If the body is able to do this rapidly enough then there may be no lasting physiologic or anatomic changes. But by the beginning of the Disease phase it is no longer able to heal the injury and return to a completely healed state. By the time the Chronic Disease stage is reached permanent injury to systems, organs and tissues has occurred.

DIS-STRESSED AND STRESSED OUT

Early in the stage of Dis-Stress many people find themselves experiencing an assortment of vague symptoms. They may experience symptoms such as generalized discomfort, anxiety, fear, nervousness, difficulty sleeping, abdominal distress, indigestion or constipation. The individual tends to be more prone to low-grade illness and infections as well as conditions such as colds, flus and allergies. The person may overeat and become overweight or even obese. They may have a loss of appetite or lose weight. They may exercise to excess, drive badly, argue a lot, lose friends and get into problems at work or in other important parts of their life. Generally, these problems are marginal and only affect them on a limited basis. Frequently recovery is rapid and in the beginning at least, the situations may be few and far between.

This level of Dis-Stress is usually associated with mental-emotional symptoms such as non-specific or mild anger and some feelings of hostility or even mild depression. The stressed individual might also experience a sense of feeling jumpy, tense, pressured or even feel "*stressed out.*" Often the Dis-Stressed person will assign these feelings to getting older, or working too hard or financial problems. Generally, he will experience the cause of his feelings as being outside of himself. "My boss is working me too hard," or "The business isn't doing too well." It is rare for people to see their role in relation to decisions they have made or belief systems they hold.

> **STRESS CAN BE CREATED THROUGH THE WAY WE LIVE OUR LIFE.**

As the process evolves the Dis-Stressed individual's often experience recurring or continuous distress, "I just never feel right" or "I always feel under the weather." They may find it difficult to get to sleep or stay asleep. Often their mind is thinking, racing, planning and plotting. When they do finally fall asleep they may have disturbing dreams, toss and turn or wake up frequently. Since a large amount of energy is expended by the hyperactivity of their mind, which appears to be "going 24 hours a day," they may feel "burned out" or exhausted during the waking part of the day. The above symptoms are commonly associated with some element of depression, occasionally a loss of appetite or even increased appetite. If these symptoms persist long enough the affected person may find himself in a state of chronic fatigue or depression.

The feeling of being out of balance, "I am not myself," is what leads us to the name of the process Dis-Stress. Something is wrong and they do not know what it is. While aware that they may have unresolved conflicts, they often are not able to recognize that these conflicts are the cause of their problems nor that these internal conflicts underlie what is happening to them. They tend to ignore or suppress what they do know about these conflicts.

When asked if they are aware that they have problems that might cause stress they will generally respond that they have no problems at all or that the problems they do have, couldn't be responsible. However, their symptoms contradict this. Since the stresses which lead to Dis-Stress are almost always caused by *a difference between the way they want the world to be and the way it actually is.* Those in Dis-Stress are rarely aware of what they believe or the conflicts that they have created for themselves. Often there is more than one problem affecting them and generally they are approaching overload from dealing with these conflicts.

Eventually the resulting Distress is best relieved by solving the underlying problems or by putting them in proper perspective and eliminating the faulty belief systems that initiated the process to begin with. The Dis-Stress phase is handled poorly by most individuals. They either live with it and suffer or they use over-the-counter medications such as antacids, aspirin, antidiarrheal, sleeping pills or wake up pills to try to control the symptoms. They may blame their diet or believe they need more rest. They often complain about their life and their problems but generally do little about them.

> STRESS IS DIFFERENCE BETWEEN
> THE WAY THEY WANT OUR WORLD TO BE,
> AND THE WAY IT ACTUALLY IS.

Another characteristic of this stage is the fact that most people will only rarely go to see a medical doctor. When they do, no specific findings or diagnosis can be made. Usually the doctor will give them vague, nondescript reasons for feeling the way they do. They may be told that they are suffering from stress and to take some time off or to go away for a brief vacation. The doctor will frequently give his patients a prescription. However, these medications are generally low-level medications only one to two steps above over-the counter medications. Laboratory tests are generally not taken and when they are, they are always negative.

One of the major tragedies associated with Stress-Related Disorders™ often begins during this phase. People who are under stress can quickly develop a propensity to become addicted to almost anything that will lower their stress levels. During this phase many people fall victim to addictions to drugs (prescriptive, non-prescriptive or even street drugs), alcohol, cigarettes, gambling, sex, affairs, cheating, stealing, shop lifting or acting out. In fact, they can become addicted to just about anything that will, for even a moment or two, relieve their stress. It makes little difference how long this relief from their stress lasts. Typically, they get immediate relief but within a short while the stress returns. Their stress may even be worse afterward, for the very thing they did to reduce their stress may end up actually worsening it or causing more damage. Since the original problem is not solved, as soon as what they did wears off, the stress level rises once again.

Most people are entirely unaware that they are becoming addicted. They will deceive themselves and others. They will argue and disagree that what they are doing to relieve their stress is right and swear it is not an addiction. They may know that their drinking, drugs, or affairs are not the answers and that they may even be wrong or immoral, which increases their level of guilt and shame. This knowledge can lead to self-reproach which in turn raises their overall stress levels. As stress levels increase they need to repeat whatever they had done, or add something new, to once again reduce their stress. This cycle, along with the addictive effects of the substances used or act performed, lead to a downward spiral, taking them deeper and deeper into addiction and farther away from problem solving.

The medical profession, the government and the legal establishment, not being aware of Stress-Related Disorders™, lump all people who are addicted into one group. This further worsens the problem as stressed individuals are often not only poorly treated, but are forced to believe through our society's propaganda that they are the dregs of the earth. Although it is absurd, addicted individuals may believe this propaganda and this further pushes them to completely lose track of what is really happening.

Many people also become addicted not only to prescription medications, but to visits to doctors visits or even therapy. The risk of addiction is lowest in the Wellness stage and gradually becomes greater in each succeeding stage. The predisposition to become addicted is often related to individuals' hopelessness about solving their problems.

PROBLEMS NOT SOLVED
CREATE STRESS
AND THIS CAN LEAD TO CHRONIC
STRESS, ILLNESS AND DISEASE.

SUMMARY

Stress is created by the lies, guilt, shame and faulty belief systems and decisions we make during the day to day process of living life. This leads to conflict which activates the stress mechanism. Eventually, if these conflicts are not resolved the

Intelligence of the body acts to force the individual to recognize that these conflicts require solution.

The body acts in the only way it can by creating physical, emotional or spiritual signs and symptoms. These are indications of the underlying conflict. At first they merely whisper but as time passes the body may begin to scream out by producing illness and later disease. We refer to the lowest level of this process as the Dis-Stress stage.

This process is an intelligent attempt by the body to communicate its needs. If the conflicts are resolved, the body will reverse the process and return to wellness.

Recognizing not only that Stress-Related Disorders™ exist, but also how they work and how they can be identified, could help thousands, maybe even millions, of people reclaim their lives. Through proper evaluation and understanding this process problem could be solved and illness prevented.

CHAPTER III

THE DIS-EASE STAGE

DIS-EASE: WHAT IS IT AND HOW IS IT RECOGNIZED?

The differences between Dis-Stress and Dis-Ease can only be appreciated when they are viewed as a series of gradually escalating signs and symptoms moving away from total wellness and toward full-blown disease. Here stress and problem solving each act as polar opposite forces. As problems and conflicts increase, stress also tends to increase. It is not unusual therefore for the signs and symptoms to become progressively more dramatic and menacing. As the individual solves the problems of his life, stress decreases. However, when he fails to solve his problems, stress increases and he may move down the continuum toward illness and disease.

Until the symptom progression reaches the stage of Disease the signs and symptoms are relatively generalized. The process, however, may be moved along or transformed suddenly when new stresses are added or old stresses coalesce to form new patterns. At these points' one may suddenly leap from a lower level to a higher level of illness. In the language of the medical profession they may "take a turn for the worse." The Stress-Illness process can literally take any form of physical, mental, emotional, or spiritual symptoms. It need not act rationally because small stresses can, in the end, have large repercussions.

It would be impossible at this point to list all of the conditions seen in the Dis-Ease stage. However, we have provided several lists in Appendices A, B and C that name a number of the more common ones associated with stress. The differences in degree and specific patterns change as the conditions continue to advance. It is difficult to define which ones belong to which stage until they have reached the Disease stage and can be listed in fully recognizable disease patterns.

To give an example, an individual who is in the earliest stages of Dis-Stress might experience only slight nausea, mild indigestion and occasional melancholy. As he moves closer toward the Dis-Ease stage he might experience an increasing degree of indigestion, bloating after meals, gas and occasional episodes of constipation or diarrhea as well as slightly deeper and longer lasting episodes of depression. As the Dis-Ease stage becomes more fully established, the symptoms may include intermittent abdominal pains, recurrent headaches or episodes of increased or irregular heartbeat. While he may barely notice some symptoms, others may well occupy a good portion of his time. One individual may have occasional but severe headaches and yet hardly notice the abdominal discomfort and associated nausea he experiences at the time of the headache. Another person may not notice an increase in his heart rate until it is brought to his attention by a pounding sensation in his chest. This variability, while part of the process, often leads the individual to think of those symptoms as a specific process (for example, headaches) and totally miss the very general nature of the early stress mechanism.

As the process progresses it can move in any number of directions. For example, it can change and move toward increasing abdominal pain which later turns into a peptic ulcer. Or it may move toward headaches accompanied by moderate elevation of blood pressure which eventually turns into full-blown hypertension. One might also experience a worsening of depression and fatigue or even frequent episodes of anxiety or panic attacks. Headaches, which initially appeared as tension headaches, might change direction and become true migraine headaches. Another person might start out with recurrent upper respiratory infections, allergies, muscle strains and injuries, low back pain or neck pain, which progress to an actual disease process involving these symptoms.

As the individual moves deeper into the Dis-Ease stage it is likely that he will need to use over-the-counter medications for relief of his symptoms. The media, the medical profession, mother, father and just about everyone they talk to will tell them not to suffer, to take something to feel better or to go to a doctor. Since over-the-counter medications are the easiest and most available they are often used first in an attempt to eliminate the symptoms. These medications, however, are not designed to cure anything. They only cover up the symptoms of stress. By relieving the symptoms, the urgency for solving the underlying problems which caused the stress is removed. By taking these medications he also covers up the body's message, this reenforces societal beliefs that these symptoms are not important or that they are caused by something that comes from outside of us (flus, job, work load, etc.) It also acts to discredit the body and its attempt to get us to listen to it.

Thus, the messages the body has been sending falls on deaf ears. Unheard, the body has little choice but to eventually escalate the level of the process.

Sometimes the conflict is buried so deep that the affected individual has little or no idea that it even exists. Hence, without an understanding of the Stress-Illness process, he has no way of knowing what is happening to him. He may do everything he can to treat his symptoms but never do anything about the underlying conflicts. He may spend years searching for miracle cures or trying to live with his afflictions and discomfort when suddenly, "out of the blue" he finds himself with a life-threatening illness.

Others procrastinate in solving their problems. They may labor over solutions without finding one; they may struggle with changes they know they should make and yet make none. Their level of illness may increase so slowly over so many years that the transition from one stage to the next is hardly noticed. What began initially as the vague and varied symptom patterns of Dis-Stress, eventually turn into Dis-Ease, then Disease and finally into Chronic Disease.

Another individual may also live with his conflicts for a while and then solve them. Or over time, his problems may lose power and "for no explainable reason" they may appear to spontaneously heal themselves. On occasion this may appear to coincide with a visit to his doctor. Many people wait until they are ready to give up their problems and conflicts and then, without consciously understanding what they are doing, suddenly decide that *now* is the perfect time to seek medical attention. Sometimes the simple act of making an appointment with the doctor is sufficient evidence to the body-mind that they are ready to let go of the problem. Healing can then occur spontaneously.

The medical doctor is not usually consulted in the early stages of the Dis-Ease phase because the signs and symptoms are relatively mild and present no significant problem. However, as symptoms become more persistent there is a steadily increasing likelihood that the affected individual will seek medical attention. As he moves into the deeper part of this stage, the symptoms usually become even more uncomfortable and threatening. He is likely to see his doctor with ever increasing frequency. He no sooner resolves one illness when he finds himself returning to the doctor's office for a new illness or recurrent problem. For years we've heard patients say things like, "It seems like I live in the doctor's office." Often these individuals are in the mid to late portion of the Dis-Ease stage. In the early years of our practice the reason these people were returning so frequently wasn't clearly understood so we simply dealt with the problem at hand and sent them on their way. Today, we recognize this pattern as a sign of an advancing Stress-Illness process. Now long before the stressed individual can reach the stage of Dis-Ease we work with their unresolved stresses and their hidden conflicts.

Since the early signs and symptoms of the Dis-Ease stage do not manifest an easily recognizable pattern, usually no conclusive medical diagnoses can be made. This fits closely with still another characteristic of this stage, the fact that whenever laboratory and diagnostic tests are performed, X-rays, blood tests, bowel studies and other such testing, they are either negative or borderline. They are never positive for any specific disease process.

During the early portions of this stage it is common to find doctors prescribing low level prescriptive medications. Generally, the main goal of treatment is the relief of uncomfortable symptoms. Here again, however, the use of medication often prolongs recovery. If, instead of using medications the messages from the body were recognized and used to uncover hidden conflicts, the illness process could be stopped. With resolution of these conflicts permanent wellness can once again be established.

VAGUE, UNCLEAR, NONSPECIFIC
SYMPTOMS ALWAYS SUGGEST A
STRESS-RELATED ILLNESS.

Another conspicuous indication of a Stress-Related Disorder and specifically of the Dis-Ease stage is that the individual rarely improves significantly with Interventive medical care.

This is generally missed by the medical practitioner since he frequently sees his patient for a series of symptoms. He concludes that he "cured" the last illness. He therefore overlooks another important sign, the *variable or changing symptom pattern* of the Dis-Ease stage. Since he is not able to put the whole process together, he often misses what is happening.

After a while, the patient's lack of progress and his frequent visits cause both patient and doctor to become unhappy. The doctor knows his patient doesn't have a disease, but since he knows little about Stress-Related Disorders™, he chooses to believe that he is either missing something or that his patient is a hypochondriac or even a malingerer.

Another indication that a Stress-Related Disorder exists is when the physician recognizes that something unusual is going on *but he just can't quite put his finger on what it is*. The patient, on the other hand, continues to suffer symptoms which he registers as illness, but he is not getting either answers or solutions.

Eventually he may lose faith in his doctor and begin looking to alternative medical practitioners such as chiropractors, nutritionists, herbalists, massage therapists, acupuncturists, family counselors, etc. Often his new practitioner will suggest changing his life style, diet, increasing exercise, giving up addictions such as alcohol, cigarettes, gambling, affairs, compulsive buying, lying and cheating. He will also give the sufferer new hope. Since the patient generally does not see the alternative medical practitioner as an all powerful healer but rather as a person who is more like himself, fallible, he does not attach the same power of "cure" to his new practitioner that he did to his medical doctor. No longer expecting a medical doctor to "cure" him, he makes up his own mind that *he* will do anything and everything to cure himself. While this may seem like a small point, for many it is the turning point in the healing process. Often this change in intention is enough to reduce stress and resolve problems.

To the degree these alternative practitioners help people relieve their immediate stress, their symptom pattern improves and the process either slows down or reverses. Many individuals become addicted to the alternative treatment program as it helps them reduce stress levels to a point where their symptoms and their life are both once again controllable. However, alternative healers frequently do not believe in illness but rather cure. Consciously or unconsciously they lead their clients to sufficient insight to their problems and conflicts that a "cure" ultimately occurs. Generally, alternative practitioners perform treatments which improve nutrition or act to balance disturbed energy patterns. This leads to a restoration of physical and nutritional harmony and balance. This differs from the patient relationship with the Interventive physician who has little time to talk, believes in illness, has no time to help solve problems and values only objective scientific evidence and treatment of symptoms with medication or surgery.

The stressed individual may actually begin to eat better, do more exercise, work less stressfully, give up addictions and do other things which reduce stress levels enough to reverse the Stress-Illness Process. It is unfortunately not unusual for people who have lived through great stress to attach their recovery to the specific program they used rather then to their own work or changes in the way they live their lives. Frequently on the television we hear someone extolling the benefits of a juice diet, fasting or Chinese herbs or telling how acupuncture or chiropractic treatment changed their lives. While all of these programs have merit for resolving specific problems, only rarely are they the "real reason" why the illness or Dis-Ease process reversed itself. If real changes are not made these results will only be short lived and the individual soon "falls off the wagon" only to start searching for some new panacea.

Even after many years of debate between the supporters of Standard-Interventive medicine and proponents of so-called "Holistic" Alternative medicine, no one is clear about what really works. One side presents testimonials of cures from their treatments. The other side presents horror stories of people who got worse or even died after those treatments. In the end everyone is confused as to what really works.

The reason for this confusion is clear: neither side really understands the real problem. When stress is relieved illness is reversed, when it is not illness progresses. The winners are the ones that are treating the right problem, the losers those who are not.

Both sides are using various similar rituals (office visits, examinations, medical treatments, injections, surgery, exercise, meditations, dietary regimes) and sacred objects (medications, herbs, vitamins, special foods, fitness equipment) to help the stressed individuals reduce their stress so that they can cope with their immediate conflicts. However, there can be no lasting success if the underlying conflicts are not found and eliminated.

If we were able to educate people about the role that day-to-day stress plays in causing illness and disease we could accomplish much more. We could prevent many people from getting ill in the first place. We could help each other solve the problems which produced conflict and this would reverse the Stress-Illness process.

HOW DIS-EASE FARES IN THE INTERVENTIVE MEDICAL SYSTEM

As the individual moves deeper into the Dis-Ease process the signs and symptoms become more and more problematic. Because the medical examination and diagnostic laboratory tests are generally negative, the Interventive medical doctor is not able to understand what is happening. His medical training teaches him only about the Disease stage when the pattern of signs and symptoms are defined and laboratory and specific diagnostic testing are positive. The Interventive medical doctor knows little about stress and almost nothing of the processes we have just discussed. For this reason most of the Intelligent cries of the body go unheeded and illness and disease flourishes in our society.

As the patient reaches the more advanced levels of the Dis-Ease stage, the medical practitioner often becomes more confused. The symptoms are almost at the level of disease, but all tests, with the exception of some non-specific testing procedures, are negative.

Since the doctor is unaware of the process we have outlined, he often believes that the only option he has is to treat his patient with medications. The specific medications he chooses can vary greatly. Some doctors tend to treat only the predominant symptom pattern. Others treat all symptoms and many use what is commonly referred to in the medical profession as a "shot-gun" approach. That is, they will treat the signs and symptoms which occur at any given moment with a wide variety of medications including moderate to high-level[6] prescriptive medications such as antibiotics, pain relievers, tranquilizers, mood elevators, sleeping pills, psychotropic drugs and whatever else seems appropriate.

Many doctors suspect that their patients are experiencing significant stress, but instead of assisting the patient in solving their problems they simply put them on psychopharmacologic medications to eliminate the symptoms. Many of these patients are maintained on medications for years, even though they become dependant on or even addicted to these medications. Many patients have adverse reactions to these medications causing the need for other medications to either reverse their effects or cover them up. Generally, no solutions are found and no problems are solved. Their inability to solve problems usually forces them to remain in unhealthy relationships or jobs they hate. It limits their income and maintains their low self-esteem. Families are destroyed, children become unhealthy and lives are lost.

It is not unusual for an individual in a particularly severe state of Dis-Ease to be on anywhere from three to twenty different medications. It is also not unusual to see more new medications added with each new symptom as the Stress-Illness process advances. Many of these individuals will experience side reactions, adverse affects and allergies from the prescribed medications or from interactions between them.

Still another indication of Stress-Related Disorders™ occurs when the primary medical doctor or the patient, himself, realizes that he is getting nowhere and the physician refers the patient to another doctor, usually a specialist or an associate. The specialty to which the patient is referred depends on the complex of symptoms which appear to predominate. It could be an Ear, Nose and Throat specialist or an Internist, Gynecologist, Neurologist, Neurosurgeon, Psychiatrist, Psychologist or some other field of specialty. This generally means that a new examination will be performed and that laboratory and diagnostic tests will be repeated. In the end, just as before, nothing is found. The consultant will often send back a report stating that he can find nothing wrong with the patient.

The primary doctor is now even more confused. Often one or more specialists or other doctors are consulted. While this may seem like a blatant abuse of the medical system it is essential to remember that all Stress-Related Disorders™ must be considered to be "real" and warrant complete medical evaluations until it is absolutely clear *that no disease* is present. All systemic and organic disease must be ruled out before beginning treatment for Stress-Related Disorders™.

On occasion the primary doctor will refer his patient to a psychiatrist or psychologist who understands the basic concepts of Stress-Related Disorders™. Effective treatment is instituted and the patient improves. The problem, however, is that most psychiatrists and psychologists do not understand stress. They involve themselves only in the psychological symptoms without following the physical signs and symptom trail. They usually have little knowledge of what we call Body Symptom Language™. Since the body cannot communicate in words it must communicate in the only way it can: in signs and symptoms, each of which represents a clue to the nature of the underlying conflict. The body often gives us many clues. To understand what the body is trying to communicate one must notice the pattern of the symptoms and then compare them to the conflicts and problems he has in his life.

Another trap is poor communications between primary doctor and the psychologist, psychiatrist and other alternative medical practitioners. This difficulty significantly reduces their capacity to help the stressed person. The psychologist or alternative practitioner is usually unknown to the medical doctor and vice versa. Hence, the patient is not getting the full benefit of a team approach to help him. This lack of communication between practitioners can lead to conflicting treatment and poor results, which may add additional stress to the patient's already heavy burden.

Since the patient usually wants an answer, more doctors are consulted and more tests are done. With each new encounter his hopes go up and then, when no answers are found, plummet to the ground. While he continues to seek help he may start to believe that he will never get well. Consider the message this gives to his body and its defensive and immune systems.

Eventually he may be told that his complaints are "all in his head." The doctors may lose interest in him and his problems. By this time he or his insurance company may have spent thousands or even tens of thousands of dollars.

As time passes he begins to rely even more on home remedies, faith healers, religion and alternative medical approaches. He may get more relief from these methods than he has from medical treatment. Usually, though, results are temporary. Since the original problem is neither found nor resolved, his stress is not relieved and pressure builds. Jobs, marriages, relationships and children are adversely affected. The patient not only loses hope but begins to worry more than ever about his situation.

By this point the individual has reached a place where he is learning how to live with his illness. The illness may become the focal point of his life since he has learned how to cope with his stress and problems rather than to resolve his underlying conflicts. He may no longer be able to recognize them as problems. He suppresses fear, anxiety, anger and lives a life of contained unhappiness. If he is good at this, he may maintain the process for the rest of his life without either getting better or worse. More commonly, however, he is not good at containing or coping with his stress and the process continues. His symptoms become more and more of a problem. They occur with greater frequency and begin to localize into one or two organ systems or become systemic involving the entire body.

PROBLEMS NEED TO BE SOLVED

The source of harmony in life is solution. When we solve problems and keep our life uncluttered and filled with challenge we feel healthy and alive. However, this breaks down when we are no longer able to solve problems. This often leads to an imbalance in the major aspects of our life; the Self, family, work, physical, mental and spiritual aspects of our life. When we allow one part to get out of balance in relationship to the others our life loses its overall harmony and balance.

There are three biological mandates built into our being. The first is the mandate to survive (the Survival Mechanism), the second is the drive to procreate (the Mating Dance™) and the third, and equally important mandate, is the drive to attain our highest and best Self. These three mandates drive the human species and are the prime forces for creating both illness and greatness. When we are out of balance in the major aspects of life this loss of balance can become our teacher. It can tell us where and how we have lost our way and how to reestablish balance in our life once again.

> **DISEASE IS OFTEN THE END RESULT OF OUR LYING TO OURSELVES ABOUT WHO AND WHAT WE ARE.**

We are part of a vast Intelligence which has given us our Intelligence. If we are not blocked, we are always growing, learning and creating. Since our life is always open to us the only thing that stands in our way is "lying" to ourselves about who and what we are. It is these lies or faulty belief systems, that are most commonly responsible for the development of our stress. When we can find these lies and faulty belief systems, learn the truth and grow from the experience, all stress will disappear.

> **WHEN SYMPTOMS, LABORATORY TESTS AND PHYSICAL FINDINGS DO NOT MATCH, A STRESS-RELATED DISORDER (SRD) MAY BY THE CAUSE OF THE PROBLEM.**

SUMMARY

Stress-Related Disorders™ are generally associated with certain characteristic complaints including anxiety, depression and other vague symptoms which act like classical diseases. The energy drain created by the stresses of our life can be identified early. If conflicts are not resolved, the Wellness-Stress-Illness Mechanism is invoked. In the Dis-Ease phase laboratory and diagnostic testing are almost always normal. If, however, the physician is confused and unable to find the originating conflict the patient may seek alternative care.

If the underlying conflict is not recognized and treated then the process will soon begin to alter the body's chemistry and anatomy. Eventually abnormalities will be found in laboratory and other diagnostic testing. The symptoms and findings may still not act totally like classical disease but at this point they get closer.

If the cause is recognized and treated the stress symptoms will resolve and the problem will disappear. If the cause is not eliminated then the process may continue until it creates a full-fledged state of Disease.

CHAPTER IV

DISEASE AND CHRONIC DISEASE STAGE

THE DISEASE PROCESS

The human body has many layers of defensive systems which continuously guard and protect it from invasion. When these defensive systems are fully activated, we experience little or no illness or disease. When they break down, illness occurs and intervention from the outside may be necessary to preserve life. In most cases' illness occurs because of the body's inability to defend itself from disease. A partial failure of the immune system (reduced bodily resistance) may allow viruses, bacteria, and other parasites to gain a foothold. Impairment of the antibody antigen system allows allergic reaction. Alterations in the defensive systems might allow cancerous tissues to grow unabated or tissue defense systems to attack our own bodily tissues such as in auto-immune diseases. Failure of our healing system may prevent the repairs which are necessary for our body to return to its natural state of normalcy after an insult or injury.

WELLNESS

IS OUR

NATURAL STATE OF BEING

Our mind is intimately connected to our body's defensive, healing and repair systems. What we think and believe can make a great deal of difference in the ability of these systems to function normally and maintain our overall health and wellness. If we are able to give our body-mind clear and decisive orders to strengthen and support our defensive and healing systems, we can rely on them to protect our health.

If the mind is involved with constant negative thinking, depressive thoughts, or is confused and operating from unclear instructions or miscommunications then it is likely there will be chaos and our body-mind will not be capable of performing optimally. This discord will eventually lead to inappropriate maintenance as well as substandard healing and inadequate repairing. If our thoughts are negative and destructive about yourself or others or if we see things outside of us as threats to our *desired* existence, then this message will be transmitted to the body-mind. This may transmit a message that we are surrounded by enemies and under attack which could activate our defensive systems as well as the stress mechanism.

If we see our self as powerless against our job, parents, neighbors and society in general, the message we will communicate is that everything and everybody is stronger than we are then we are powerless. This can occur even if we are not consciously aware that we hold such negative or fearful feelings and thoughts. This message may cause the defense system to falter and allow pathologic organisms to enter, take hold and create disease. Fear, anger and rage can be the basis for allergic disorders, auto-immune diseases, diseases of the heart and other vital organs and even cancer.

> OUR BODY IS A FORTRESS, IMPENETRABLE
> TO ALL BUT THE
> MOST AGGRESSIVE OF
> ORGANISMS.

No matter what our history has been or what we have believed in the past we are always really in control of what our mind is allowed to spend time on or give power to. We must make it a point to stay in charge and not let it out of our conscious control. To do this we must have a clear picture of who and what we are. It is important that we become responsible to ourselves to solve problems and not to allow conflicts to impair our defensive and immune systems.

In its earliest stages, the disease process[7] is part of the internal wisdom of the body which is built into all of us to protect and teach us what we need to know about ourselves. This would be well and good if we "got the message" and solved our conflicts. Unfortunately, most people, including many medical doctors, either ignore these symptoms and signs of the internal conflict or see them strictly as "medical problems." They are treated with medications or other medical or surgical treatments. If left unresolved, these conflicts drive the Stress-Illness process until the stage of Disease is established.

> ILLNESS IS ALWAYS A SIGN OF UNRESOLVED
> CONFLICT.
>
> SOLVE THE CONFLICT AND THE ILLNESS
> GOES AWAY.

Once we enter the Disease stage the process is taken over by the specific disease mechanism itself. It begins to act in accordance with the laws and rules which govern its own process. From this point on, the course of action moves farther and farther away from our best interests. The ability of our Intelligent body to maintain control is compromised. Eventually, the disease takes over its own destiny and has a "mind of its own." It is usually at this point that medical treatment becomes essential, where previously it might have been unnecessary.

Of the stages we have discussed, the Disease stage is generally the easiest to recognize. While the symptoms may not be notably different from those of the Dis-Ease stage, we can now, for the first time, identify it by positive findings at the time of a medical examination. We now also have positive laboratory and/or diagnostic test results. The medical history, however, if carefully analyzed is essentially consistent with multiple stressors, unresolved stresses and a progressive pattern of signs and symptoms which are consistent with the progression of the Stress-Illness process.

These positive signs, symptoms and testing now direct the medical doctor to specific organs or tissue areas and a definite diagnosis can be established. At this point the medical doctor, for the first time feels he is on solid ground, now he knows where he is and what he can do for his patient. It is unfortunate, however, that this process has been allowed to get this far before the patient's medical doctor could help him effectively.

Now a "definitive" treatment program can be prescribed in the form of medications, surgery or other medical therapies. The medications are more likely to be specifically directed at the now defined condition. They are also usually of greater therapeutic value than medications used in earlier stages. In the early Disease stage the patient will usually get good results from this directed treatment regime. However, he may not continue feeling better.

The particular illness process may be relieved yet the underlying problems and conflicts are rarely resolved through standard Interventive medical treatments. New stresses may have been added and the individual can fall right back into the same illness or a new illness once treatment is terminated. One way a new illness may appear is in the form of *complications* involving the original condition. Medical treatment may be revised, new medications are added and old ones discontinued. Quite frequently the patient spends the rest of his or her life taking medications to manage symptoms. Because the underlying conflicts which led to the stress were not resolved, forces in the unconscious are left to smolder and burn.

While the medical doctor may feel himself on solid ground, the patient frequently does not. In the end the patient is continuously taking medications, being treated but not healed. Over time he may lose some level of function. He may require surgery, lose time from his job and have less quality time with his family. As old conflicts reignite and new conflicts are added his condition may eventually deteriorate from an acute condition to a state of Chronic Disease.

CHRONIC DISEASE

Once the Stress-Illness process reaches the earliest stages of Chronic Disease the situation is well on its way to becoming irreversible. This loss of reversibility means that it may no longer be completely cured simply by solving the original problem. The disease process which had taken on a life of its own is now taking away the life of the individual it has overpowered. It is also now entirely separate from its original causes. Most medical doctors think of this transition as an unfortunate situation. Many doctors do not see this as their failure but as a failure on the part of the patient, his body, his genetics or his inability to follow instructions. Caring doctors will wonder what they might have missed, what more they could have done, or if they could have done things differently. Few look past the obvious physical problems to see what caused them to begin with.

Usually, by the time the process has reached the stage of Chronic Disease, it has had an effect on the patient's family. Thousands of dollars have been spent for doctor's visits, hospitalizations, medications, diagnostic testing (laboratory, X-ray, CT scans, MRI and other such testing). There have been the additional costs of time from work, a loss of savings or retirement funds and possibly the cost of special appliances. In many cases even more surgery is needed. Special equipment (breathing machines, blood sugar testing equipment, wheel chairs) and physical therapy, respiration therapy or psychotherapy may also become essential for survival.

> ONCE A CHRONIC DISEASE
> STATE OCCURS,
> THE CONDITION IS NEITHER
> REVERSIBLE NOR CURABLE.

The most important question to be asked is, "Could all of this be prevented in some way?" The answer is often yes. Stress-Related Disorders™ can generally be prevented when the process is recognized early enough, especially when it is recognized prior to the onset of the chronic disease stage. The big problem is that so few people are able to recognize their stress induced conflicts early enough to make a difference.

The Chronic Disease process also follows along the lines of Body Symptom Language™. However, our lack of understanding of this process often leads us to miss what is happening. Instead, we react to the immediacy of the symptoms rather than looking for the causative problems.

For example, an individual with chronic back pain may have developed this specific condition because his body is trying to tell him that he is unhappy with his job and it represents a heavy burden he is no longer able to carry. He may have even thought to himself, "What I am breaking my back for?"or something like that for years prior to his first back pain or his first injury. For him to suffer the anger and discomfort the job causes him is dangerous. The job doesn't support him in reaching his highest and best Self. His back pain therefore may be from his anger, helplessness, loss of self-value, inability to stand up straight and strong or to take care of himself. However, since he is unable to hear the warning cries from his body, he is likely to have to injure himself or become so ill that he is ultimately no longer able to work. He may end up having to restrict his activities or having to be taken care of.

None of this is conscious. It is all mediated through his stress system because the body-mind sees the job as a threat, an accident may occur, he may be injured on the job or he may suffer pain and disability for no apparent reason. Finally, his body-mind gets what it wants. His pain and disability cause him to lose his ability to work and function normally on that job. Unfortunately, his mind-body had to get what it wanted the hard way for he is now crippled.

A person stressed by a long history of financial problems and not finding his true sense of himself (another way of referring to his highest and best Self) may find himself with a peptic ulcer. For years his mounting bills and inability to pay them and do what he wants with his life have been "eating him alive." Years earlier he may have only suffered minimal symptoms such as acid indigestion, burping and bloating. However, over the years these symptoms gradually progressed until eventually he begins to have recurrent abdominal pains and gastritis. All of the previous signs and symptoms were attempts by his body to tell him that he must resolve his conflicts. Since he wasn't able to hear them and solve his problems he ultimately developed an ulcer[8]. The ulcer itself is just another clue, a reminder that his conflicts still exist and are actively evolving.

Another person who holds buried anger at his treatment by a parent allows his helplessness and rage to eat at him. The origin of the conflict having been long since suppressed into his unconscious, he might suddenly find himself fighting cancer. His cancer is a sign of the suppressed rage which has been devouring him for years. He probably had many other signs and symptoms of this process along the way but ignored them, and now his rage is killing him.

In each of these situations, years of unheeded messages and failure to recognize and solve conflict ultimately undermined the defensive and immune systems as well as the healing and repair systems of the body. Our negative feelings and lack of action send a message of *weakness and inability to function adequately.* Anger sends a message of being *eaten up, devoured, corrupted, or of weakness and helplessness.* This may declare to the body that life is too hard and that it is *no longer worth living.* The body interprets these messages as commands that *it is not worth it* to defend itself or that *it is a failure.* It will then fail to protect us adequately by allowing infections in or malignant cells already in our body to flourish.

The body may even read these negative messages as an indication to attack its own self. These individuals may have dreams where they are being chased, overpowered, surrounded or feeling helpless or lost. They may say or think negative, destructive, demeaning thoughts over and over again all through the day. They may feel or think they are overwhelmed or out of control. Generally, they do not recognize these thoughts as being negative instructions to the body. But the mind-body sets in motion a process which creates exactly what it thinks we are asking for. This is the basis of the Stress-Illness-Disease process.

THE HIGH COST OF CHRONIC LIFE-THREATENING DISEASE

The financial, physical, mental, emotional, spiritual and family costs of chronic illness are great. However, these are not the only costs. They frequently lead to a burden on our whole society. The overall growth of industry is slowed down, small businesses are hurt, there is often a drain of talented people. Ultimately, health care premiums and taxes must be raised to pay for the increased costs of health care. The burden on the taxpayers is also greatly increased because of the people who become indigent, poor and disabled from their Stress-Related Disorders™.

If underlying causes of these chronic illnesses are not resolved, no lessons will have been learned. If the process reaches the stage of Chronic Disease then we will have missed the most important lessons of our life, possibly even the essence of our life. We will have missed an important opportunity to grow.

The ultimate penalty for missing this message is death. Each year hundreds of thousands of people around the world die needlessly from illnesses that could have been prevented. "Who is to blame?" No one and everyone. While we may recognize that this can happen, most of us still ignore it. Worst of all is when we ignore what is happening to us or to one of our loved ones.

Up until the stage of Chronic Disease the Stress-Illness process is generally fully reversible. Once the stage of Chronic Disease is initiated, it is at best only partially reversible. In the next chapter we will see how we can return to wellness if we don't wait too long

SUMMARY

As the immune system fail's external organisms are allowed to enter into the body cause infection and injure tissues. The immune system also may attack turn and attack the body. As the body turns against itself disease is created. Laboratory testing becomes positive, while the doctor is now able to diagnose the time is late and complete reversal will soon be impossible if correct action is not taken.

CHAPTER V

RETURNING TO WELLNESS

THE JOURNEY HOME

It is likely that the conflict which was responsible for the onset of the individual's stress no longer exists by the time he reaches the stage of Dis-Ease. By the onset of the Disease stage it has probably been long forgotten. This means the present events are being fueled only by memories from the past or new stresses which are not being resolved. If the triggering conflict no longer exists how can it still be relevant and important? It would seem that most of our conflict and stress should have been erased over the years. In fact, this more than likely would be true if it weren't for the power we give to these memories.

Those events and situations which threaten us are often retained by the body-mind to help insure our survival in the future. We retain memories of painful events to protect us from similar events occurring in the future. If, however, we give power to these negative processes, we can maintain them for years and they can affect us and the way we live our life on a daily basis. If they cannot be controlled, they can propel us into the Stress-Illness process and to an unnatural conclusion. To eliminate stresses we have found that *all* levels of conflicts must eventually be mastered. The individual must be transformed into a full-fledged problem solver.

Our ability to create or to return to wellness depends almost entirely on our willingness to solve the problems which originally precipitated our stresses. To do this we may need to learn a number of new techniques which can help us manage the future conflicts of our life. When we suffer a mild illness, we may still feel relatively well. In fact, we may not want to believe that this illness has any significance to us. If the illness is self-limiting and runs its course, healing may be spontaneous and complete. Yet, we may wonder where it comes from or whether something could still be wrong underneath. These thoughts generally come from our innate recognition that to get ill one or more of our many levels of defensive systems must have been breached and that there may well have been inner help for this to occur.

If we regain our health we are often quite willing to ignore what has happened and return to the business of living. If we get a new illness or the same illness reoccurs we may become so involved with our discomfort or fear that we are unwilling to ask the necessary question, "Why is my body not protecting me?"

When we have one illness after another, healing often depends on our ability to recognize that some part of our physical, mental, emotional or spiritual self is out of balance. It may indicate that we still have ongoing conflicts that need to be solved. Knowing that 70% to 80% of the time our symptoms, regardless of how they appear, are related to stress should suggest that we look for the stresses in our life.

> SYMPTOMS AND SIGNS, ALONG
> WITH THE AREAS AND TYPE OF
> ILLNESSES AND DISEASE ALL
> CONTAIN INFORMATION FOR US.

GETTING WELL AGAIN

The Stress-Illness process can be reversed. Reversing stress requires that the individual do whatever is necessary to solve the problems and conflicts that have caused it. It is possible, however, to take a partial or limited approach, one where commitment is not complete but there is a willingness to try. In this situation, however, one may not get a full reversal of the illness process.

It is important at this level to become fully acquainted with the power of positive thinking and to realize that when we allow negative thought we undermine positive action. In both positive and negative forms, thoughts act as a kind of prayer activating our unconscious body-mind (our lower self) and our spiritual self (the Higher Self), to work together to either promote healing or to delay it. By concentrating on positive, healing thoughts and by solving problems we activate the most powerful aspects of our healing and repair systems. This also has a positive affect on our defensive and protection mechanisms.

THE ILLNESS-STRESS-WELLNESS MECHANISM - REVERSING THE ILLNESS PROCESS

While most people with either acute or chronic illnesses want immediate reversal of their illness, this will only happen as fast as they are willing and capable of allowing it to happen. (See Figure: 2, below, an outline of the Illness-Stress-Wellness
Mechanism.) Just as with Stress-Related Disorders the Wellness-Stress-Illness Mechanism this indicates the process by which illness caused by stress is reversed and we are returned to wellness.

It is important that healing Stress-Related Disorders™ be a combined effort of Standard Interventive medicine and Integrated medicine practitioners. Once the illness is evaluated and the diagnosis of Stress-Related Disorder has been made, the patient should be educated as to what stress is and how it can cause the problems they are experiencing. The more we learn about stress the easier it will become for us to let go of our fear and anger and begin the process of searching for the underlying causes.

ILLNESS-STRESS-WELLNESS MECHANISM

SOLVE PROBLEMS AND ELIMINATE CONFLICTS —>
REVERSAL OF DISEASE (ACUTE OR CHRONIC) —>
DIS-EASE —> DIS-STRESS —> STRESS —>
WELLNESS

Figure: 2.

We must then learn some simple techniques to help us find the causes. These techniques include ways of listening to our body and what it has to say to us, as well as communicating with our inner self, experiencing emotions that have been blocked and suppressed and increasing our self-image and self-esteem.

This educational process should help teach us the difference between a worsening of the disease process and the exacerbation of unresolved conflicts. As layer upon layer of conflict are unearthed, which we refer to as *peeling the onion,* there are bound to be times when deeply hidden conflicts will suddenly pour out and create havoc. When it is realized that this is not only expected but desired, we will be able to use this out-pouring to our advantage.

As the pressure and tension are released, the level of illness will decrease from the stage of Disease to Dis-Ease, then to Dis-Stress, then to non-specific or generalized stress and eventually, to complete and total wellness. This reversed process is often missed by patient and practitioner alike. When recovery is not as rapid or steady as is desired this returning to wellness may confuse and undermine their resolve. Generally, it is more common to see slow steady improvement rather than sudden cures. How long each phase lasts is dependant upon the extent of the conflicts left undetected or unsolved and the willingness of the individual to find them and maintain the healing process. For some people, solving the worst and most life-threatening situations happens instantly. For others, resolving relatively meaningless conflicts can take a lifetime.

If the process is done right there is a realization that stress is a friend and can be used to learn from and to promote growth. Those who learn this well are less susceptible to Stress-Related Disorders™ in the future. At its highest level of success we become a seeker of the truth of who and what we are and embark on a journey that takes us to our highest and best Self. At this level the concept of illness is meaningless.

To the unenlightened practitioner, a sudden reversal of illness is confusing and impossible and his only way of rationalizing it is to call it a *miracle.* To the enlightened practitioner this sudden resolution only means that the individual either solved his conflict or decided that it no longer has power over him. The most enlightened healers know that virtually *all illness and disease* can be overcome. While some disorders or disabilities cannot be reversed, healing can create a new vision of the Self which allows the individual to rise above his disability and find his highest and best Self.

For most people, wellness and the ability to control their own life and destiny makes the journey and everything they have gone through worthwhile.

SUMMARY

Wellness is a state of harmony and balance between the major aspects of our life and our three selves. Healing occurs when we create this to happen. The job of healing does not belong to the physician but rather to the sick person himself. When the physician stops practicing medicine and begins caring for and supporting his patients to heal their conflicts, resolve their problems and integrate their mind, body and spirit. Then and only then is the physician a true healer.

Miracles are dramatic evidence of how healing works. Both physician and patient must work together to maximize results. The for both goal is finding, nourishing and optimizing the evolution of their highest and best Selves.

Appendices

APPENDIX A

PHYSICAL MANIFESTATIONS CAUSED BY OR ASSOCIATED WITH STRESS

GENERAL
Rashes (acne) and/or hives
Frequent bouts with flu-like symptoms (possibly related to lowered immune system and body resistance) / more colds than normal
Cold, clammy hands and/or feet
Increased sweating
Increased appetite and obesity
Inability to work / sudden bursts of uncontrollable energy
Faintness / dizziness / numbness / paralysis

IMMUNOLOGIC
Allergy
Reduced resistance to infection
Tumor promotion
Auto-Immune Phenomena

EXTREMITIES / MUSCULAR / SKELETAL SYSTEMS
Muscle aches (especially neck, shoulders, back or legs) cramping / tightness
Unexplained fatigue / muscle weakness / lethargy
Arthritic-like joint pains
Neck pain / backache / sharp momentary shooting pains
Numbness /paralysis of extremities

HEAD / EYES / EARS / NOSE / THROAT
Headaches / migraines / tension / sinus headaches
Frowning or frequent wrinkling of the forehead
Dry mouth / bad breath / difficulty swallowing Jaw clenching / jaw pain / bruxism / tenomandibular joint syndrome
Teeth gnashing / grinding

Facial tics and twitching
Eye "strain" / Changes in visual acuity
Ringing in the ears

RESPIRATORY / CARDIOVASCULAR SYSTEMS
Cackling, hacking cough
Rapid heartbeat / irregular heartbeat / arrhythmia
Chest pains / shortness of breath / angina-like symptoms
Hyperventilation

GASTROINTESTINAL SYSTEM
Nausea / vomiting / diarrhea / constipation
Stomach or abdominal pain
Acid indigestion / reflux of acid into esophagus (Gastroesophogeal Reflux or GERD)
Irritable Bowel Syndrome
Diarrhea / Constipation Bloating / biliousness

URINARY !REPRODUCTIVE SYSTEMS
Frequent urination / difficulty starting and stopping urination
Discomfort on urination / impotence
Irregular Menstruation / menstrual cramps / skipped menstrual periods / absent menstrual periods
Premenstrual Syndrome
Menopausal Symptoms

COMMON BEHAVIORAL AND OTHER MANIFESTATIONS CAUSED BY OR ASSOCIATED WITH STRESS

GENERAL

Insomnia / nightmares / frequent day dreaming Increased or decreased appetite Increased or chain smoking

Frigidity / loss of sex drive / obsessive sex drive

Addictions Constantly thinking / rehashing / rehearsing / worrying

EMOTIONAL

Flutters of fear / anxiety at odd moments / feeling on edge / feeling jumpy / feeling out of control / feeling tense / nervousness / anxiety or panic episodes

Feelings of frustration / inability to define reason for frustration / an awareness that while organized and working hard, you are not producing or accomplishing much.

Waves of anger / feelings of hurt and disappointment / depression / irritability / bad temper

Crying episodes / laughing episodes for no apparent reason.

Altered moods / feeling like you are living in a fog or that there is a cloud or curtain separating you from your life / nagging

Feeling you must always have something to do, you can't sit still and enjoy life

PHYSICAL

Unconscious foot or finger tapping / nail biting / scratching or picking at body / pacing / restlessness / unnecessary hand waving / wild gestures

Persistent ache "in the center of you"

Stuttering

DIGESTIVE

Eating problems / obesity / anorexia

MEMORY AND THOUGHT PROCESS

Memory slips / loss or inability to remember familiar names and faces / reduced instant recall / reverie / reliving past experience instead of dealing with the present.

Difficulty concentrating / must continually re-read material both personal and work related / inattentiveness / shortening of memory or attention span

Foggy thinking / racing thoughts / impaired judgement

Indecisiveness / feeling confused / fear of making decision

The knowledge that "the little problems" you've been experiencing disappear completely when you are absorbed in a movie or something very pleasurable but return immediately when the activity is over.

STRESS-RELATED DISORDERS™

GENERAL/METABOLIC SYSTEM
Hypoglycemia, hyperthyroidism,
worsening or triggering of
diabetes
Acne, hives, rashes
Neurodermatitis
Asthma, bronchitis
Obesity
Chronic Fatigue Syndrome

PSYCHIATRIC
Post-traumatic stress syndrome
Neurosis
Transient situational disturbances
Depression
Anxiety, Panic attacks

MUSCULOSKELETAL
Tension headache
Migraine headache
Low, Mid and Upper Back pain,
Neck pain Injuries, accidents and
strains

CARDIOVASCULAR
Coronary artery disease
Heart attack
Stroke
Hypertension (high blood pressure)

GASTROINTESTINAL
Peptic ulcer disease, gastritis
Ulcerative colitis Irritable bowel
syndrome
Constipation, diarrhea

IMMUNOLOGIC
Reduced resistance to infection
(Colds, flu, viral, parasitic
illnesses and other minor
illnesses of all sort)
Allergies (All types.)
Tumor promotion, benign and
malignant

URINARY / REPRODUCTIVE

SYSTEMS
Failure to menstruate, excessive
menstruation
Infertility
Fibroid tumors
Impotence
Premature Ejaculation
Incontinence
Bladder and Prostate infections.

JUST ABOUT EVERY ILLNESS AND
DISEASE HAS A STRESS COMPONENT.

EITHER AS A CAUSE OR AS AN EFFECT.

STRESS-RELATED DISORDERS

Footnotes:

1. See Appendices A through C for a more extensive listing of Stress-Related Disorders™.

2. If the reader is interested in reading more about Huna and its relationship to modern medicine we refer them to our soon to be published book *Huna—Ancient Healing Miracle Practices and the Future of Medicine*.

3. The pain is stored in our emotional center within the lower self.

4. We use the term *illness* to refer to vague symptoms or conditions which, while uncomfortable, are not harmful. When we refer to *disease* we are usually suggesting a more defined condition, one which can cause harm or lasting injury. The medical profession and most people generally use these terms interchangeably. By explaining our usage we hope to reduce confusion.

5. It is only productive when we have turned our problems into solutions or when we have learned from the experience and grown in some way. This can only happen when we are able to convert whatever is creating our stress into challenge and therefore into an opportunity to find a solution.

6. That is, medications which are potentially dangerous, have significant side affects, allergic reactions, adverse reactions and negative affects when combined with other medications.

7. Specifically Stress Related Disorders and possibly all illnesses and diseases.

8. The concept of Body Symptom Language™ would suggest that an ulcer is a specific clue not only to the fact that stress exists, but also to the type of stress the individual is experiencing. The body can only relate to its owner in signs and symptoms.

Printed in Great Britain
by Amazon.co.uk, Ltd.,
Marston Gate.